THE MONKEY AND THE CRABS

さるかに合戦

THE MONKEY AND THE CRABS

さるかに合戦

Compiled by Sayumi Kawauchi
Translated by Ralph F. McCarthy

川内彩友美 編

ラルフ・F・マッカーシー 訳

講談社インターナショナル
KODANSHA INTERNATIONAL
Tokyo · New York · London

本書について

　「さるかに合戦」は「日本五大昔ばなし」のひとつ。登場するものが多少ちがったかたちで、日本各地に伝わっています。

　悪がしこいさるにいじめられ、けがをさせられて死んでいったお母さんがにのかたきをとろうと、子がにたちはさるをやっつけに、いさんで出かけていきます。その子がにの話を聞いて手助けを申し出る、くり、はち、牛のくそ、うす……。作戦はみごとに成功しました。弱いものでも、おたがいに協力し、長所を生かして立ちむかえば、たとえ自分よりずっと強い相手でも倒すことはできるのだということを、教えてくれています。

Published by Kodansha International Ltd.,
17-14 Otowa 1-chome, Bunkyo-ku, Tokyo 112-8652.

The Monkey and the Crabs
Text and illustrations copyright
© 2000 by Ai Kikaku Center.
English translation copyright
© 2000 by Kodansha International Ltd.
All rights reserved. Printed in Japan.
First Edition, 2000
00 01 02 03　10 9 8 7 6 5 4 3 2 1
ISBN4-7700-2650-1

About This Book

"The Monkey and the Crabs"[1] is one of the "Five Great Folktales of Japan."[2] Variants[3] of this tale, often with somewhat different characters,[4] are told in every part of the land.

The baby crabs bravely set out[5] to take revenge on the crafty monkey[6] who bullied and fatally wounded their mother.[7] Offering to help[8] after hearing their story are a chestnut, a bee, a cow pie, and a mortar[9]…Their plan succeeds brilliantly.[10] The story teaches us that the small and weak,[11] by working together and making use of their strong points,[12] can defeat even the most powerful enemy.[13]

---

[1] The Monkey and the Crabs さるとかに [2] Five Great Folktales of Japan 日本五大昔ばなし [3] Variants 勇者たち [4] with somewhat different characters 登場するものがいくぶん違う [5] bravely set out いさんで出かけた [6] take revenge on the crafty monkey ずるいさるをかたきうちする [7] bullied and fatally wounded their mother お母さんがにをいじめてけがをさせ、死なせてしまった [8] Offering to help 手助けを申し出る [9] a chestnut, a bee, a cow pie, and a mortar くり、はち、牛のくそ、うす [10] Their plan succeeds brilliantly 作戦はみごとに成功します。 [11] the small and weak からだが小さく、弱いもの [12] making use of their strong points 長所を生かすこと [13] can defeat even the most powerful enemy どんなに強い敵でも倒すことができる

Once upon a time somewhere,[14] there lived a mother crab who was very hungry.[15]

"If I don't eat, the babies in my tummy[16] won't grow![17] I'd better go find[18] some food."

むかしむかし、あるところに、おなかをすかせたお母さんがにがすんでいました。

「なにかを食べないと、おなかの子どもが育たないし、さて、食べものをさがしにいくことにしましょう。」

---

[14] Once upon a time somewhere むかしむかし、あるところに [15] very hungry おなかをすかせた [16] the babies in my tummy おなかの中にいる子どもたち [17] won't grow! 育たないでしょう [18] I'd better go find さがしにいくことにしましょう

Just then[19] a very rude monkey[20] came along,[21] juggling[22] two delicious-looking persimmons[23] he'd found.

The hungry crab stared at[24] the persimmons.

"You want 'em?[25] They're really good…"

そこへ、おいしそうなかきを二つ手にして、お手玉遊びをしながら、らんぼう者のさるがやってきました。

おなかをすかせたかには、じいっとそのかきを見ていました。

「食いたいか……。おいしいぞう。」

[19] Just then ちょうどそのとき　[20] a very rude monkey らんぼう者のさる　[21] came along やってきた　[22] juggling お手玉遊びをしながら　[23] delicious-looking persimmons おいしそうなかき　[24] stared at をじっと見つめる　[25] You want 'em? 食いたいか ('em=them)

The crab was thrilled,[26] thinking he was going to give her the fruit. But the monkey just threw a persimmon seed at her.[27]

"Eat that!" he said.

Wasn't that mean of him?[28]

"Hee, hee, hee![29] Mmm…Tasty!"[30]

The monkey ate the second persimmon, too, right in front of the crab.[31]

かきをくれるのかとよろこんだかにのところへ、

「これでも食らえ！」

と、さるはかきの種を投げつけました。

まったく、いじわるなさるですね。

「ひひ……、ああ、うまい。」

さるは、もう一つのかきも、かにの目のまえで食べてしまいました。

---

[26] was thrilled わくわくした　[27] just threw a persimmon seed at her かきの種を投げつけただけだった　[28] Wasn't that mean of him? なんて、いじわるなさるなんでしょうね。　[29] Hee, hee, hee! ひひ　[30] Tasty! うまい！　[31] right in front of the crab かにの目の前で

³² sidled off sadly がっかりして、こそこそ立ち去る ³³ to look once again for food また食べものをさがしに ³⁴ finally とうとう ³⁵ A big riceball 大きなおにぎり ³⁶ lay on the ground 地面にころがっていた ³⁷ I saw it first! わたしが先に見つけたんですよ。 ³⁸ clung for dear life to her prize ひっしでおにぎりにしがみついた

So the crab sidled off sadly[32] to look once again for food.[33]

And then, finally,[34] she found something. A big riceball[35] lay on the ground[36] before her.

But the monkey saw it, too.

"I saw it first!"[37] The crab clung for dear life to her prize.[38] "It's my riceball!"

かには、すごすごと、また食べものをさがしにいきました。

そのときです。かには、やっと見つけました。大きなおにぎりが、目のまえにころがっていたのです。

ところが、さるもそれを見つけてしまったのです。

「これは、わたしが見つけたものです。」

かには、ひっしでおにぎりにとびつきました。

「わたしのにぎりめしだ！」

The monkey grinned as he approached.[39]

"Hee, hee! Won't you give it to me?"[40]

"No! It's mine![41] It is!"

"In that case,[42] Mrs. Crab, let's trade.[43] I'll give you this persimmon seed."

"I can't eat something like that!"[44] the crab said angrily.[45]

さるは、にやにやして近づきます。

「ひひひ、そいつをおらにくんねえか。」

「だ、だめです。わたしのよ。これは。」

「そんじゃ、かにさん、とりかえっこしねえか。そうだ、このかきの種と。」

「そんなもの食べられないじゃないの。」

---

[39] grinned as he approached にやにやしながら近づいた [40] Won't you give it to me? そいつをおらにくれないか [41] It's mine. わたしのよ。 [42] In that case そういうことなら [43] let's trade とりかえっこしよう [44] I can't eat something like that. そんなもの食べられないわよ。 [45] angrily おこって

⁴⁶ plant 種をまく　⁴⁷ crafty monkey ずるいさる　⁴⁸ you can grow 育てられるよ　⁴⁹ Before long そのうち　⁵⁰ it will be loaded with~ ~がどっさりなるぞ　⁵¹ more sweet, sweet persimmons than you can eat 食べきれないほどの、あまい、あまいかき　⁵² Once you've eaten a riceball おにぎりは食べてしまえば　⁵³ that's the end of it, right? それっきりだ、そうだろ。　⁵⁴ with that そういって　⁵⁵ placed おいた　⁵⁶ snatched ひったくった　⁵⁷ began gobbling it down ばくつきはじめた　⁵⁸ Oo-ee! ひゃあ　⁵⁹ gazed bitterly at をうらめしそうに見つめた　⁶⁰ so upset that tears filled her eyes あんまりくやしくて目に涙がいっぱいうかんだ

"But if you plant[46] this," said the crafty monkey,[47] "you can grow[48] a persimmon tree. Before long[49] it'll be loaded with[50] more sweet, sweet persimmons than you can eat.[51] Once you've eaten a riceball,[52] that's the end of it, right?"[53]

And with that[54] he placed[55] the persimmon seed on the ground, snatched[56] the riceball, and began gobbling it down.[57]

"Oo-ee![58] It's good!"

The crab gazed bitterly at[59] the monkey. She was so upset that tears filled her eyes.[60]

かにがおこると、ずるいさるはいいました。

「こいつをまけば、かきの木がはえてよ。そのうち、食いきれないほどのあまーいあまい実が、どっさりなるんだぜ。おにぎりは食べてしまえばそれっきりだもんな。」

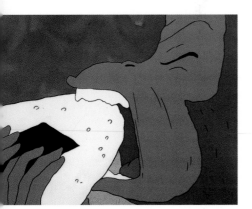

さるは、そういって、かきの種をおくと、さっさとおにぎりをぱくつきはじめました。

「ひゃあ、うめえ。」

そんなさるを、うらめしそうに見るかに。くやしくてなみだが出てきます。

17

But what could she do but plant the seed?[61] With her last ounce of strength[62] she dug a hole[63] in the ground, dropped the seed inside, and covered it with dirt.[64] Then she peered at[65] the dirt and chanted with all her heart:[66]

"Sprout up now,[67] persimmon seed!

If not,[68] I'll pinch you right in two!"[69]

And, believe it or not,[70] the dirt began to wriggle,[71] and up popped a sprout![72]

"Become a tree,[73] persimmon sprout![74]

If not, I'll pinch you right in two!"

The crab clacked her pincers[75] as she watered[76] the sprout.

---

[61] But what could she do but plant the seed? でも、かにには、種をまく以外に何ができたでしょう。 [62] With her last ounce of strength 最後の力をふりしぼって [63] dug a hole 穴をほって [64] covered it with dirt それに土をかぶせた [65] peered at をじっと見た [66] chanted with all her heart いっしょうけんめい何度もよびかけた [67] Sprout up now いますぐ芽を出せ [68] If not そうしないと [69] I'll pinch you right in two! はさみでまっぷたつにちょんぎるぞ。 [70] believe it or not なんとしたことでしょう（信じられないことに） [71] wriggle もぞもぞとうごめく [72] up popped a sprout! ぴょこんと芽が出てきたのです。 [73] Become a tree 木になれ [74] persimmon sprout! かきの芽よ！ [75] clacked her pincers はさみをちょきちょき鳴らした [76] as she watered 水をかけながら

18

　しかたがありません。かにはかきの種をうえることにしました。かには最後の力をふりしぼって、くわをふるい、穴をほり、かきの種をうえました。
　「早く芽を出せ、かきの種。
　出さぬと、はさみでちょんぎるぞ。」
　かにはいっしょうけんめい、地面に向かって声をかけました。すると、地面がもぞもぞして、芽が出てきたではありませんか。
　「早く木になれ、かきの芽よ。
　ならぬと、はさみでちょんぎるぞ。」
　かには、小さな芽に水をかけながら、はさみをちょきちょきさせました。

⁷⁷ right before her eyes かにの目の前で ⁷⁸ shot up ぐんぐんのびた
⁷⁹ Bear fruit now いますぐ実をつけろ ⁸⁰ as if hearing her plea かに
の願いを耳にしたかのように ⁸¹ the big tree's branches filled with
green fruit 大きな木の枝々に青い実がどっさりなった ⁸² redden 赤く色づく
⁸³ ripening into delicious-looking persimmons 熟しておいしそうな
かきになった ⁸⁴ hard work had finally paid off やっと、骨折りが報わ
れた

And right before her eyes[77] the sprout shot up[78] and became a big tree.

"Bear fruit now,[79] persimmon tree!

If not, I'll pinch you right in two!"

And, as if hearing her plea,[80] the big tree's branches filled with green fruit.[81]

Soon the fruit began to redden,[82] ripening into delicious-looking persimmons.[83]

All the crab's hard work had finally paid off.[84]

芽は、みるみるうちに大きくのびて大きな木になりましたよ。
「早く実がなれ、かきの木よ。

ならぬと、はさみでちょんぎるぞ。」
かにのねがいが通じたのか、大きな木に青い実がどさーっとなりました。
青い実はだんだんと色づいて、おいしそうなかきになりました。やっと、かにの努力が実ったのです。

　「そろそろ食べられるかな──。」

と、かにが木にのぼろうとしたのですが、あれれ、せっかくのかきの実に手が

とどきません。

　そこへあらわれたのが、ほら、あのいじわるなさるでした。

　赤いかにも、まっ青になっておどろきました。

　「これは、わたしのかきの木です。」

---

[85] They're just about ready to eat ちょうど食べごろだわ　[86] tried to climb the tree かきの木にのぼろうとした　[87] oh, dear! あれれ　[88] were right there すぐそこにあった　[89] couldn't reach them! 手がかきの実にとどかない　[90] who should come along just then but ~ ちょうどそのときあらわれたのが、ほら～　[91] that mean old monkey あのいじわるなさる　[92] turned pale with horror 仰天してまっ青になった

"They're just about ready to eat,"[85] she said and tried to climb the tree.[86]

But—oh, dear![87] The persimmons were right there,[88] but she couldn't reach them![89]

And who should come along just then but[90] that mean old monkey![91]

The red mother crab turned pale with horror.[92]

"This persimmon tree is mine!"

⁹³ how will you どうやって〜するのかい　⁹⁴ scrambled up the tree 木によじのぼった　⁹⁵ Just leave it to me. まかしといてくれ。　⁹⁶ plucking a ripe, red persimmon 熟した、まっ赤なかきの実をもぎとった　⁹⁷ ignored 無視した　⁹⁸ took a big bite がぶりとかじりついた　⁹⁹ Mm! うーん　¹⁰⁰ How sad the crab was that 〜 かには〜なので悲しくてしかたなかった　¹⁰¹ pluck one かきを取る

"But how will you[93] get the fruit?" the monkey said and scrambled up the tree.[94]

"Just leave it to me.[95] I'll get some for you," he said, plucking a ripe, red persimmon.[96] But he ignored[97] the crab and took a big bite.[98]

"Mm![99] Delicious!"

How sad the crab was that[100] she couldn't climb trees!

"Please pluck one[101] for me, too!"

「でも、どうやってとるのかねえ。」

さるは、するすると、かってに木にのぼってしまいました。

「まあ、まかしときな。おらがとってやるからな。」

といいながら、さるは、まっ赤なかきの実をもぎとったのですが――。

かにには知らん顔で、さるは、がぶりとかじりつきました。

「う、うめえ～～～。」

かには、木にのぼれないのが悲しくなりました。

「おねがい！　わたしにもとっておくれ。」

The monkey gave her a nasty look[102] and said, "All right. I'll pluck one for you."

And he picked a green persimmon and threw it right at her.[103] The hard fruit hit[104] the poor mother crab and wounded her badly.[105] What a horrible[106] monkey!

さるは、意地悪い目でかにを見ると、

「ようし、おまえにもとってやるからな。」

と、青い実をとって、かにに投げつけたのです。かわいそうに、かたい実をぶつけられたかには、大けがをしてしまいました。なんてひどいさるでしょう。

---

[102] gave her a nasty look 意地悪い目つきでかにを見た　[103] threw it right at her かににまともに投げつけた　[104] hit ぶつかった　[105] wounded her badly 大けがをさせた　[106] What a horrible monkey! なんてひどいさるでしょう!

But the mother crab's shell[107] was broken, and out crawled[108] three cute little babies.

As soon as[109] the monkey had eaten his fill of[110] persimmons, he headed back home.[111] He acted as if[112] he'd completely forgotten[113] the mother crab he'd wounded so badly.

A few days later, the mother crab died of her wounds.[114]

The poor baby crabs![115] "We'll never forget what that mean old monkey did," they promised one another.[116] And by working hard and sticking together[117] they all managed to survive.[118]

---

[107] shell こうら　[108] out crawled はい出てきた　[109] As soon as ~ ～する やいなや　[110] had eaten his fill of を思うぞんぶん食べた　[111] headed back home すみかに帰った　[112] He acted as if ~ ～かのようにふるまっ た　[113] he'd completely forgotten すっかり忘れてしまった　[114] died of her wounds けががもとで死んでしまった　[115] The poor baby crabs! な んて、かわいそうな子がにたち。　[116] they promised one another みん なで約束をかわしあった　[117] by working hard and sticking together 努力をし助けあって　[118] they all managed to survive みんなでなんとか 生きていった

　でも、そのとき、かにのこうらがわれて、かわいい三びきの子がにが生まれ
たのです。

　さるは、たっぷりとかきを食いちらかすと、大けがのおかあさんがにのこと
なんかわすれたかのように、自分のすみかに帰っていきました。

　何日かして、お母さんがには、そのけががもとで死んでしまったのです。

　かわいそうな子がにたちは、

　「いじわるさるのことは、けっしてわすれないぞ。」

　そうやくそくして、力をあわせて生きていきました。

One day, when the little crabs were nearly grown,[119] they set out in high spirits[120] to take revenge on the hateful monkey.[121]

On the way,[122] they met up with a chestnut.[123]

"Hi-ho,[124] little crabs! Where are you going?"

"To get revenge on the mean old monkey!"[125]

The chestnut, too, had a grudge against[126] the monkey. He wanted to join[127] them.

こうして大きくなった子がにたちは、ある日、にくいさるをやっつけようと、いさんで家を出かけました。

「おいおい、子がによ、どこさいく。」

「あのいじわるさるをやっつけにいくのさ！」

---

[119] nearly grown かなり大きくなった　[120] they set out in high spirits いさんで家を出た　[121] to take revenge on the hateful monkey にくらしいさるに仕返しするために　[122] On the way 途中で　[123] met up with a chestnut くりにであった　[124] Hi-ho おいおい　[125] the mean old monkey あのいじわるなさる　[126] had a grudge against ~ ～にうらみがあった　[127] join 仲間にはいる

"All right!" he said. "I'll go with you!"

Next they met up with a bee,[128] and then a cow pie,[129] and then a mortar.[130] Each of them had a grudge against the monkey as well.[131]

So the little crabs, the chestnut, the bee, the cow pie, and the mortar all set out for[132] the monkey's house.

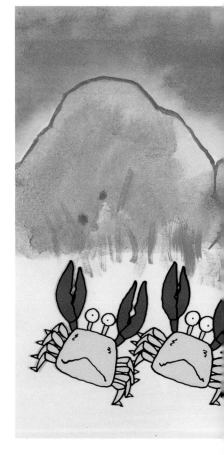

[128] bee はち [129] cow pie 牛のくそ [130] mortar うす [131] as well 同じように [132] set out for をめざして進んでいった

「ようし、おらもいく！」
　とちゅうでであったくりも、さるにうらみがあったので、いっしょにいくというのです。
　つぎにであったのが、はちどん。そして、牛のくそどんも、うすどんも、みいんな、さるにはうらみがあるというのです。
　こうして、子がにといっしょに、くり、はち、牛のくそ、うすも、さるのすみかをめざして進んでいきました。

33

¹³³ crafty and violent fellow 悪がしこいらんぼう者　¹³⁴ There was no telling わからない　¹³⁵ when or where he might attack いつどこでやつにおそわれるか　¹³⁶ decided to fly ahead 先にとんでいくことにした　¹³⁷ scout out the house 家のようすをさぐる　¹³⁸ reported しらせた　¹³⁹ wait for his return さるの帰りを待つ　¹⁴⁰ When that blasted monkey gets home あのいまいましいさるが帰ってきたら　¹⁴¹ probably たぶん　¹⁴² want to warm himself by the fire いろりにあたろうとする　¹⁴³ I'll hide in the ashes 灰の中にかくれるよ　¹⁴⁴ explode ぱちんとはじける　¹⁴⁵ burying himself between the coals 炭の間に身をうずめて　¹⁴⁶ The explosion would surely burn the monkey くりがはじけたら、さるはきっとやけどするでしょう

The monkey was a crafty and violent fellow.[133] There was no telling[134] when or where he might attack.[135] So the bee decided to fly ahead[136] and scout out the house.[137]

"The monkey isn't home!" he reported.[138]

They decided to hide inside the monkey's house and wait for his return.[139]

"When that blasted monkey gets home,[140] he'll probably[141] be cold and want to warm himself by the fire."[142]

"All right, I'll hide in the ashes[143] and explode,"[144] said the chestnut, burying himself between the coals.[145] The explosion would surely burn the monkey.[146]

さるは悪がしこいらんぼう者です。いつどこからおそってくるかわかりません。そこで、さるの家のようすを、はちが見てくることにしました。
「さるは、るすだぞうっ。」
みんなは、家の中にかくれてさるを待つことにしました。
「さるのやつ、帰ってきたら寒い寒いといろりにあたるだろう。」
「よし、ぼくが灰の中にかくれて、ぱちんとはじけてやろう。」
と、くりはいろりの灰の中へ。くりがはじけりゃ、さるはやけどです。

"He'll run to the water barrel[147] to cool his burns with water."[148]

"All right, then, I'll hide beneath the handle of the ladle,"[149] said the bee, and he did just that.[150]

「あついあついと水でひやしに水がめのところへいくだろう。」

「よし、そんじゃおらは、ひしゃくの柄にかくれて、ちくりとしよう。」

と、はちが水がめにかくれました。

---

[147] water barrel 水がめ [148] to cool his burns with water 水でやけどをひやそうと [149] beneath the handle of the ladle ひしゃくの柄の下に [150] he did just that そのとおりにした

After getting stung[151] by the bee…

"The monkey will squeal and run outside."[152]

"All right, then, I'll wait on the front step,"[153] said the cow pie. Stepping on[154] the cow pie, the monkey would surely slip and fall.[155]

"All right, then," said the big, heavy mortar, "I'll be waiting on the eaves.[156] When the monkey falls, I'll drop on top of him."[157]

The little crabs hid inside[158] the mortar.

[151] After getting stung ささされたあと [152] squeal and run outside 悲鳴をあげて外に走り出る [153] on the front step ふみ石の上で [154] Stepping on をふんづければ [155] slip and fall つるりとすっころぶ [156] eaves ひさし [157] drop on top of him さるの上に落ちる [158] hid inside の中にかくれた

　はちにさされたさるは……、
　「いたい、いたいと、外へにげだすだろう。」
　「じゃ、おらはふみ石の上で待ってやろう。」
　牛のくそどんが、こういいます。
　牛のくそをふんづけりゃ、さるはつるりとすっころぶにちがいありません。
　そこでうすどんは、こういいました。
　「じゃ、おらはひさしの上で待っていよう。ころんださるの上に、どしんだ。」
　うすの中には子がにがかくれました。

Now that they were all in position,[159] they had only to wait[160] for the monkey to come home.

They waited and waited, but the monkey didn't show.[161]

At long last,[162] when twilight fell[163] and the mountain crows began to caw,[164] the monkey returned.[165]

こうして、みんなはさるの帰るのを待ちました。

まだかな、まだかな。さるはなかなか帰ってきませんでした。

でも、山のからすが、かーかー鳴いて、夕ぐれともなると、やっとのことで、さるは帰ってきました。

---

[159] Now that they were all in position すっかりみんな位置についたので [160] they had only to wait 待つだけでした [161] didn't show 姿をあらわさなかった [162] At long last やっとのことで [163] when twilight fell 日が落ちたとき [164] the mountain crows began to caw 山のからすが鳴きはじめた [165] returned もどってきた

¹⁶⁶ Brr! ひい ¹⁶⁷ Just as they'd thought みなが思ったとおりに ¹⁶⁸ he went straight to the hearth まっすぐにいろりのそばへ行った ¹⁶⁹ Woo! やれやれ ¹⁷⁰ Just then ちょうどそのとき ¹⁷¹ red-hot chestnut まっか に焼けたくり ¹⁷² right in the monkey's face さるのかおに命中した ¹⁷³ Pop! ぱちん

"Brr![166] It's cold!"

Just as they'd thought,[167] he went straight to the hearth.[168]

"Woo![169] I'll warm myself by the fire…"

Just then,[170] the red-hot chestnut[171] exploded right in the monkey's face.[172] *Pop!*[173]

「ひい、寒いぜ、寒いぜ。」

みんなが思ったとおり、さるはいろりのそばへ……。

「やれやれ、あたたまることにしよう。」

そのとき、あつあつに焼けたくりが、ぱちんとはじけて、さるに命中。

43

"Ouch![174] It burns![175] Water! Water!"
The bee was ready for him.[176] *Zzzt*![177]
"Ow![178] Ow! Ow!"

「あちち……、水、水だあ。」
まってましたとばかり、はちは、ちくり。
「いててて……。」

---

[174] Ouch いたい　[175] It burns! あちち　[176] was ready for him さるを待ちかまえていた　[177] Zzzt! ちくり　[178] Ow! いたい

179 front door 表の戸口　180 Zooop! すってんころり　181 Thud! Squish! どすん、ぎゅう　182 that's how こうして　183 got the beating of his life さんざんに痛めつけられた　184 From then on それからというもの　185 continued to ~ ～し続けた　186 ever after いつまでも　187 Ta-da! ちゃんちゃん

The monkey ran out the front door[179] and slipped on the cow pie. *Zooop!*[180]

Down came the mortar. *Thud! Squish!*[181]

And that's how[182] that nasty monkey got the beating of his life.[183]

From then on,[184] the little crabs continued to[185] work together and help one another, and they all lived happily ever after.[186] And that's the end of the story. Ta-da![187]

戸口のほうへにげるさる。牛のふんをふんづけて、つるり。うすが落ちて、どすん、ぎゅ――。

さすがらんぼう者のさるも、こうしてさんざんいためつけられました。

それからは、子がにたちは力をあわせて、いつまでもしあわせにくらしましたとさ。おしまい、ちゃんちゃん。

注釈

横山千晶（慶應義塾大学助教授）

まんが日本昔ばなし
さるかに合戦
Once Upon a Time in Japan
The Monkey and the Crabs

2000年9月8日　第1刷発行

編　者　　川内彩友美

訳　者　　ラルフ・マッカーシー

発行者　　野間佐和子

発行所　　講談社インターナショナル株式会社
　　　　　〒112-8652　東京都文京区音羽 1-17-14
　　　　　電話：03-3944-6493（編集部）
　　　　　　　　03-3944-6492（業務部・営業部）

印刷所　　凸版印刷株式会社

製本所　　黒柳製本株式会社

落丁本、乱丁本は、講談社インターナショナル業務部宛にお送りください。送料小社負担にてお取替えいたします。なお、この本についてのお問い合わせは、編集部宛にお願いいたします。本書の無断複写（コピー）は著作権法上での例外を除き、禁じられています。

定価はカバーに表示してあります。